This Oscar book belongs to:

....

....

First published 2006 by Walker Books Ltd
87 Vauxhall Walk, London SE11 5HJ

This edition published 2007

10 9 8 7 6 5 4 3 2

This book has been typeset in ITCKabel

Printed in China

British Library Cataloguing in Publication Data: a catalogue
record for this book is available from the British Library

ISBN 13: 978-1-4063-0496-1

www.walkerbooks.co.uk

WALKER BOOKS
AND SUBSIDIARIES
LONDON · BOSTON · SYDNEY · AUCKLAND

For Poppy and Finn
G.W.

The author and publisher would like to thank Sue Ellis at
the Centre for Literacy in Primary Education and Martin Jenkins
for their invaluable input and guidance during the making of this book.

OSCAR
and the
FROG

A BOOK ABOUT GROWING

Geoff Waring

One spring day, by the pond, Oscar saw some creatures he had not seen before. Frog hopped up.

"They're tadpoles," he said.

"I was a tadpole before I grew up."

Oscar stared at Frog. He didn't look like a tadpole at all.

"Don't be silly, Frog!" he laughed.

"It's true," Frog said, and he told Oscar how frogs grow.

"At first I looked like a dot in an egg. The egg was as soft as jelly…

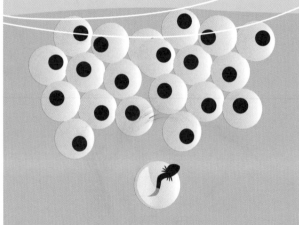

I grew in the egg, and hatched out as a wriggly tadpole.

I could breathe under water through "gills" like a fish.

I was hungry for pond weed – it helped me to grow.

Later my gills disappeared as I grew lungs to breathe air with. I grew back legs,

then front legs, and my tail started to shrink.

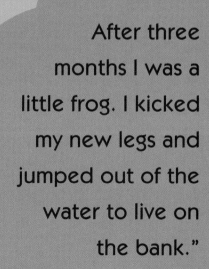

After three months I was a little frog. I kicked my new legs and jumped out of the water to live on the bank."

"What else hatches out of eggs?" Oscar asked. They looked in the pond. Frog showed Oscar some eggs that are laid in water.

Many water snails lay their eggs in pouches of jelly on stones or plants.

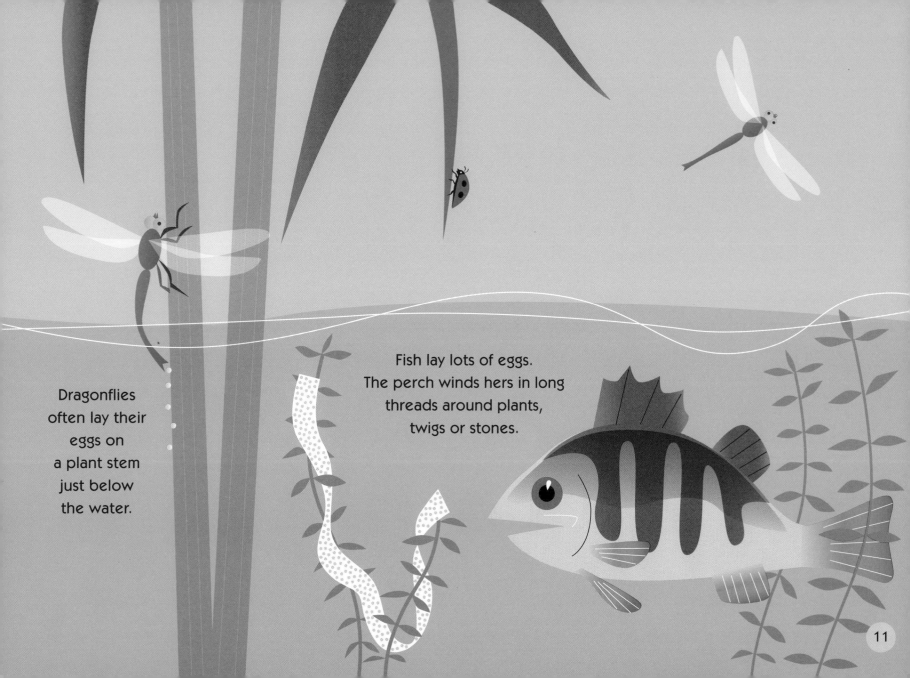

Dragonflies often lay their eggs on a plant stem just below the water.

Fish lay lots of eggs. The perch winds hers in long threads around plants, twigs or stones.

11

They looked on the bank and Frog showed Oscar some eggs that are laid where it's dry.

Many kinds of butterfly lay their eggs on the undersides of leaves. When the caterpillars hatch out of the eggs, they will eat the leaves.

Many birds nest high off the ground. Here they are safe from animals who might want to eat their chicks when they hatch.

Ducks often nest on the ground close to water, so their ducklings will be able to swim quickly away from danger.

13

"Do plants hatch out of eggs?" Oscar asked.
"No," said Frog. "Most plants sprout
from seeds. Each plant makes its
own kind of seed."

The seeds of apple trees
are stored inside their fruit.

Strawberry plants have small
seeds on the outsides
of their fruit.

Poppy plants have tiny seeds. They are light enough to be carried in the air.

Most seeds ripen above the ground. The seeds of the peanut plant grow in the earth.

Coconut palm trees have huge seeds. They can float.

"Did I hatch out of an egg," Oscar asked, "or sprout from a seed?"
"Neither," said Frog. "You were born. When you came out, you
looked quite like you do now, only much smaller – with
fur and paws, ears and a tail. You were hungry
for milk from your mother!"

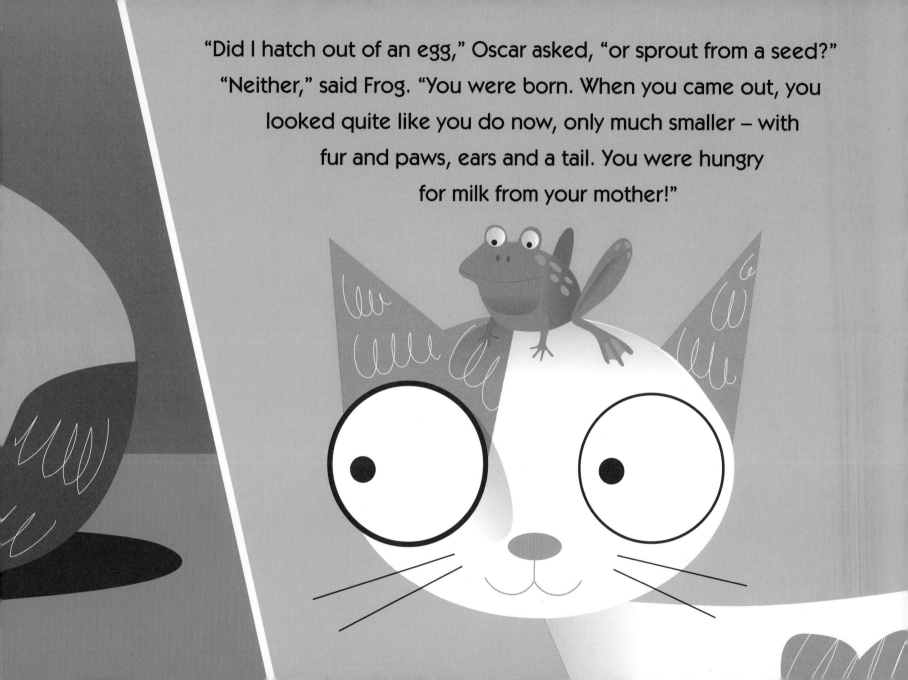

"Why was I hungry for milk?" Oscar asked.

"It helped you to grow," said Frog.

"Milk for you, pond weed for me ...

leaves for these

caterpillars ...

and bugs
for those
baby birds.
We all need
different
food to
grow."

Oscar stretched. "I am *so* big now," he told Frog. "But you're not as big as you will be," said Frog. "Are you?" asked Oscar. "Yes," Frog answered. "I've stopped growing now. I'm as big as I'm going to get."

"How long does it take to grow up?" Oscar asked.

"It depends," said Frog. "This flower will be full-grown in a few days …

but this young tree won't be tall
until you are a very old cat...

"The baby birds will be as big as their parents next spring," Frog went on, "but the tadpoles will take three springs or more to be as big as I am. Each living thing takes its own time."

Just then, Oscar saw that his mother was coming.

"What about me?" he asked Frog.
"How long will I stay a kitten?"
"You will be a
full-grown cat
by winter," Frog
said, "as big as your
mother is now."

Oscar looked at
his mother. She
was much bigger
than he was.

"Don't be silly,
Frog!" he laughed.
"It's true," Frog said.
"Wait and see!"

27

Thinking some more about growing

By the pond, Oscar found out about these things...

Beginnings

Living things begin in different ways.

Some hatch out of eggs,

some sprout from seeds,

some are born.

How did you begin? On your next walk, look out for living things that hatch, sprout or are born.

Food

All living things have to eat to grow. They need different kinds of food.

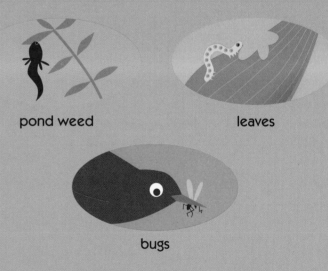

pond weed

leaves

bugs

What helped you to grow when you were very young? What do you eat that helps you grow now?

Getting bigger

Living things grow at different speeds.

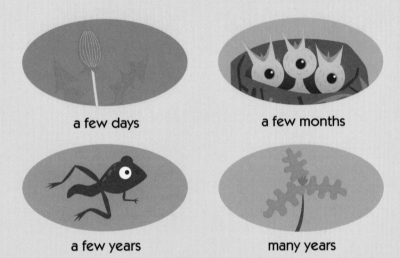

a few days

a few months

a few years

many years

How long will it take you to grow
as big as your mother?

Oscar thinks growing is great! Do you too?

OSCAR and the FROG
A BOOK ABOUT GROWING
Geoff Waring

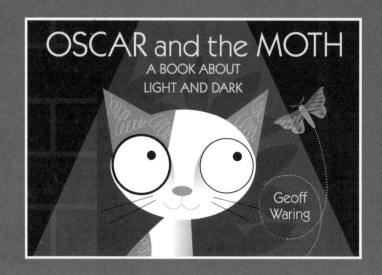

OSCAR and the MOTH
A BOOK ABOUT
LIGHT AND DARK
Geoff Waring

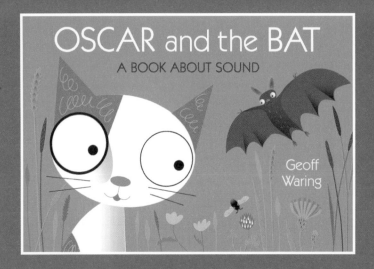

OSCAR and the BAT
A BOOK ABOUT SOUND
Geoff Waring

OSCAR and the CRICKET
A BOOK ABOUT MOVING
AND ROLLING
Geoff Waring

Which of these Oscar books have you read?